Fiela of Gold

Alison Hawes

Illustrated by Pam Smy

An old man had a lazy son.

So he told his son,

"This map shows there is gold
in that field."

The son jumped up right away.

"I will dig up the gold," he said.

He dug in the sunshine…

…and in the rain.

He dug up weeds and stones.
But he did not dig up the gold!

"You must have missed the gold,"
said the old man.

So the son dug over the field again.

As his son dug,

the old man sowed vegetable seeds.

"I still cannot see the gold!"
said the son.
"Wait and you will see the gold,"
said the old man.

As the old man and his son waited,
the vegetable seeds began to grow.

Later, a man came to the farm.
"I will pay you gold for your
vegetables," he said.

So the son quickly dug up the vegetables.

They sold the vegetables to the man.

The man paid them with gold.

"Now I can see the gold!"
said the son.

And he was not lazy again!